QUEEN NZINGA

Written by
ALEKSANDAR PANEV

Illustrated by
THOMAS STEFFLBAUER

This story is set in the late 16th century and early 17th century, in Africa. Each chapter ends with a non-fiction page that gives more information about real people's lives and actual events at that time.

OXFORD
UNIVERSITY PRESS

QUEEN NZINGA

JOÃO DE SOUZA

KAKENGO

ALFONSO

LUEJI

REAL PEOPLE IN HISTORY

QUEEN NZINGA (1582-1663): The Queen of Ndongo who fought against Portuguese slave traders.

JOÃO (zh-wow) DE SOUZA (dates unknown): The Portuguese governor of Luanda.

FICTIONAL CHARACTERS

KAKENGO: Nzinga's childhood friend who is captured by Portuguese slave traders.

ALFONSO: Kakengo's slave master in Brazil.

LUEJI: Nzinga's friend and companion.

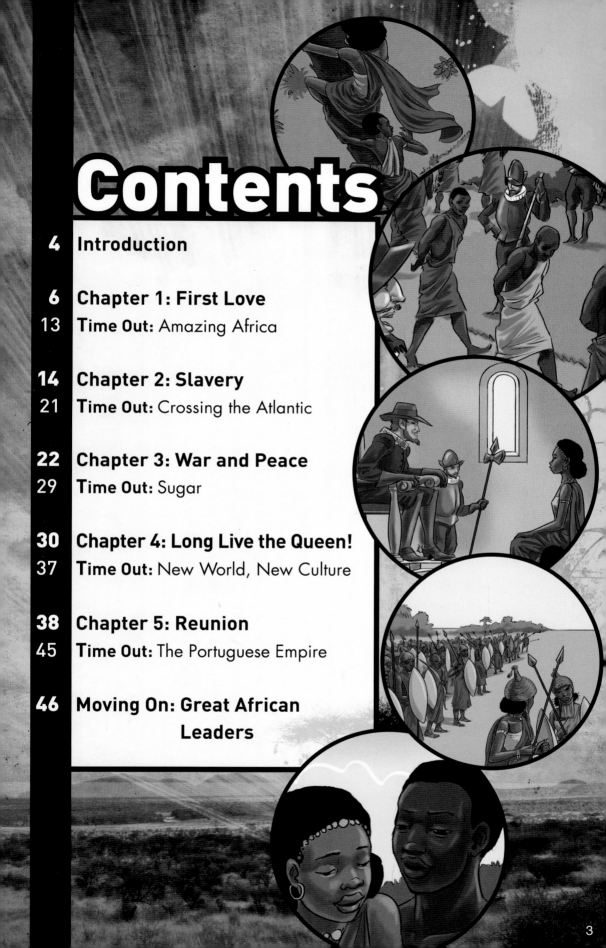

Contents

Over 500 years ago, sailors from Portugal arrived in West Africa. At first, the Portuguese stopped to get water and other supplies for their ships, but soon there was something else they wanted from Africa – slaves.

At this time, there was a kingdom on the southwest coast of Africa called Ndongo. The Portuguese often attacked Ndongo (now known as Angola) to capture slaves for their mines and plantations.

The Portuguese built a port city in Ndongo called Luanda and stationed many soldiers there. A Portuguese governor controlled the slave trade from Luanda.

In the late 16th century, a remarkable woman grew up in Ndongo. She would lead her people against the Portuguese slave traders.

Her name was Nzinga Mbande (Jinga Em-bahn-day).

Angola

1483 >>	1576 >>	1582 >>	1622 >>
The Portuguese arrive in Ndongo (now Angola).	The city of Luanda is founded by the Portuguese.	Nzinga Mbande is born.	Nzinga meets the Portuguese governor for peace talks.

A warrior in the kingdom of Ndongo

This story is set in an actual time in history, although some of the events are fictional. Real events during this period are shown on the timeline below.

1624	1644	1648	1663
Nzinga becomes Queen of Ndongo.	Queen Nzinga wins an important victory against the Portuguese.	The Portuguese gain control over Ndongo.	Queen Nzinga dies.

1594: NDONGO IS AT WAR WITH PORTUGAL. THE PORTUGUESE HAVE COME TO AFRICA TO CAPTURE PEOPLE AND MAKE THEM SLAVES. HOWEVER, IN THE PALACE OF THE KING OF NDONGO, IT IS A PEACEFUL MORNING.

PRINCESS NZINGA PLAYS IN THE GARDEN.

T-H-U-D

OUCH! WHO DID THAT?

YOU SHOULDN'T STAND UNDER A COCONUT TREE!

I CAN DO WHATEVER I LIKE! WHO ARE YOU?

THE NEXT DAY, NZINGA VISITS THE GARDEN AGAIN, HOPING TO SEE KAKENGO.

KAKENGO IS TRYING TO CATCH A RABBIT.

AMAZING AFRICA

Africa is the seat of the ancient civilisations of Egypt and Carthage, and of the great empires of Songhai, Mali and Kongo.

Africa is the birthplace of humanity, where the earliest human ancestors appeared about two million years ago.

Africa is the second largest continent after Asia, forming a fifth of the Earth's landmass.

Today, Africa is home to over 50 independent countries.

Africa is where you will find the largest desert in the world, the Sahara, and the longest river, the Nile.

Today, Africa is home to more than 840 million people who speak more than 2,000 languages.

Africa is also home to some of the most amazing animals on Earth, such as the giraffe, zebra, gorilla and hippopotamus.

CHAPTER 2: SLAVERY

Slave ship

INSURRECTION ON BOARD A SLAVE SHIP.

TIME OUT!

CROSSING THE ATLANTIC

In the days of the slave trade, ships from Europe sailed with goods to sell in Africa. They then loaded up with slaves from the west coast of Africa and sailed across the Atlantic to the Americas. After unloading the slaves, they filled up with rum and molasses and sailed back to Europe.

The journey across the Atlantic was called the Middle Passage. It was extremely long, harsh and dangerous. For up to five months, the slaves were packed like goods in the holds of the ships. Conditions were unbearable. Many tried to escape their misery by starving themselves or jumping overboard.

Chains used for slaves

21

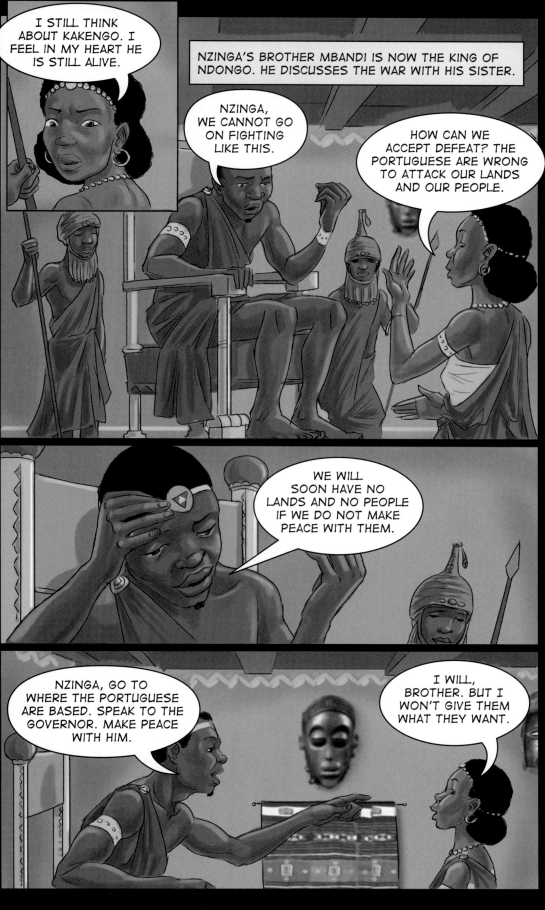

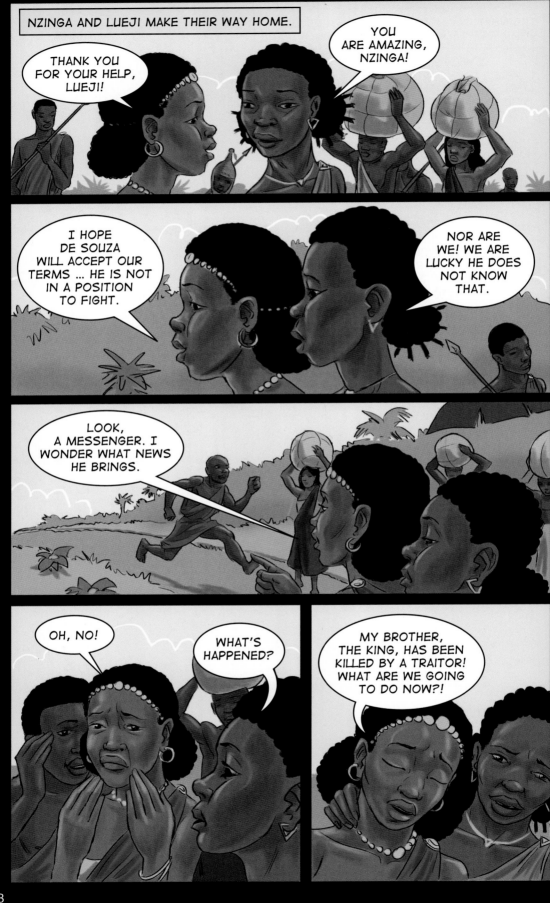

Sugar cane crop

SUGAR

Sugar was introduced to the Europeans in the Middle Ages. Before this, people in Europe sweetened food with honey.

At first, this new discovery was a luxury only the rich enjoyed. Sugar was very expensive because it had to be imported. In 14th-century Britain, one kilogram of sugar cost four shillings – more than £80 today! It was so valuable that it was stored and locked up in special containers.

Today, sugar is cheap and is used for more than just sweetening food.

- It is used in sweets and desserts.
- It is used to make glass for movie stunts.
- It can be used on cuts to aid healing.
- It is added to water in vases to help flowers stay fresher longer.

Sugar cane

THE PEOPLE OF NDONGO GREET THEIR NEW QUEEN.

NEW WORLD, NEW CULTURE

I n the New World (the Americas), slaves were far away from their homelands. They created a new culture of their own, which was a blend of old and new.

LANGUAGE: The slaves learned European languages such as English, Spanish and Portuguese, but they still used African words and expressions. Words such as jumbo, zombie and gumbo are African in origin.

RELIGION: Many slaves practised Christianity combined with African rituals such as drumming and dancing.

FOOD: The slaves combined African and European foods in their cooking. For example, gumbo is a dish made of African okra, European vegetables and American shellfish.

MUSIC: Slaves sang to relieve boredom at work. Gospel music has its roots in these working songs.

The new customs that the slaves created became important in New World countries.

CHAPTER 5: REUNION

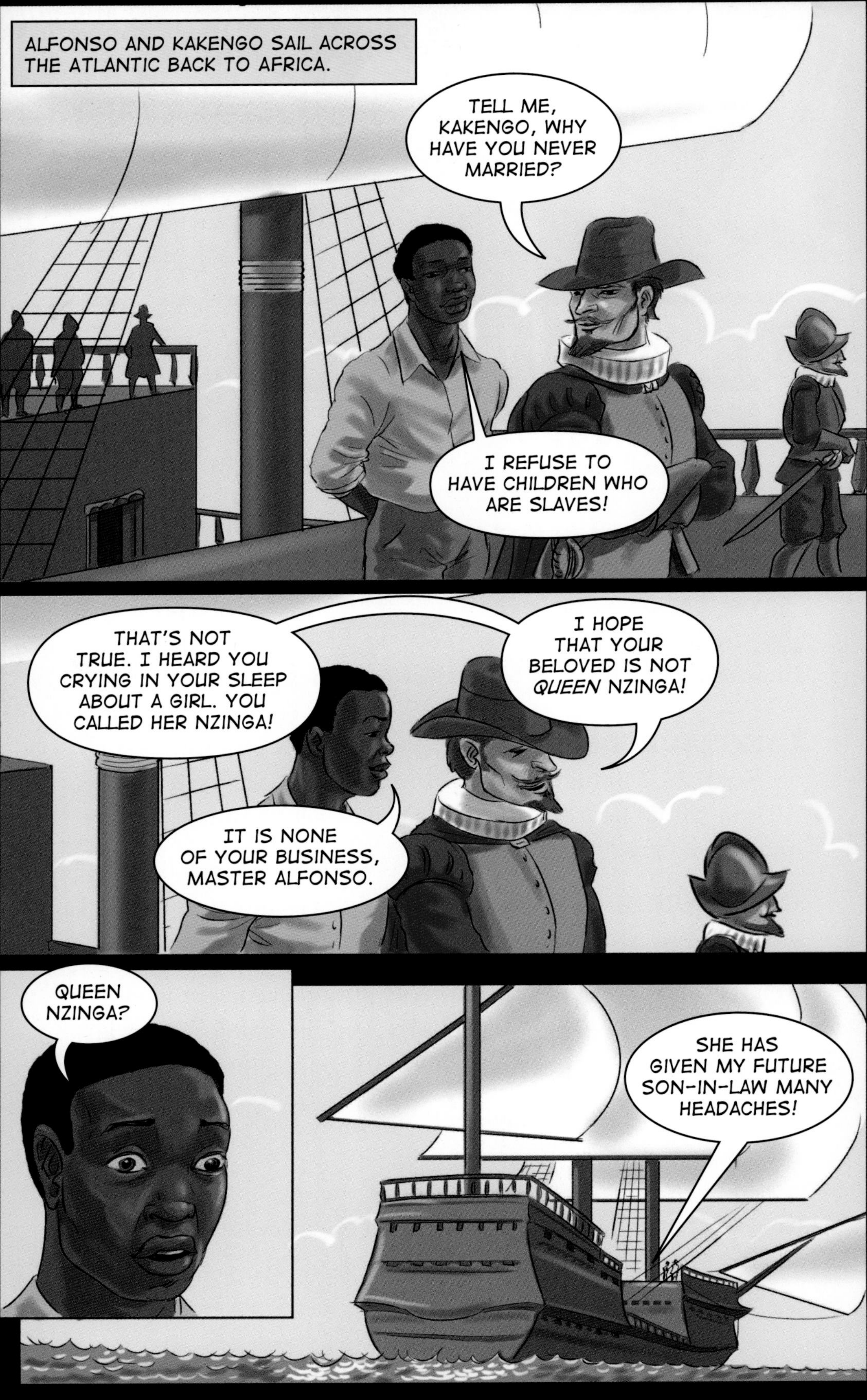

THE PORTUGUESE EMPIRE

The Portuguese were great seafarers. The first Europeans to sail the seas around Africa and India were Portuguese explorers Bartholomew Diaz (1450–1500) and Vasco da Gama (1469–1524).

In addition to exploring, the Portuguese built a world empire spanning South America, Asia and Africa. Many of these colonies were eventually taken over by Britain, France, Spain and the Netherlands.

Some territories remained as Portuguese colonies until recent times. In Africa, Angola regained independence in 1974, and Mozambique in 1975. East Timor was granted independence in 1975, but it was occupied by Indonesia until 1999.

The Portuguese empire came to an end in 1999, when Portugal formally handed Macau back to China.

Vasco da Gama

GREAT AFRI

Africa went through a long period of slavery and foreign control. Despite this, Africa and its people have played a major role in the world.

African culture has had a huge influence on popular culture, particularly in Europe and the Americas. In music, samba, blues, jazz, reggae and rock 'n' roll have their roots in Africa. What we now call rap or hip hop actually started in West Africa.

African sculptures inspired European artists in the 20th century. Picasso, the famous artist, based many of his works in the early 1900s on African art and sculpture.

Many great Africans have become inspirational leaders.

NELSON MANDELA: He fought discrimination against non-whites in South Africa and was put in jail for 27 years. After his release, Mandela became the first president to be elected by all the people of South Africa.

WANGARI MUTA MAATHAI: In 2004, she became the first African woman to receive the Nobel Peace Prize for her work in protecting the environment and promoting peace, democracy and sustainable development.

KOFI ANNAN: He first became the Secretary-General of the United Nations in 1997. As a world leader, he works for world peace, human rights and equality.

CAN LEADERS

Nelson Mandela and his supporters

African drums

INDEX

GLOSSARY

alliance – an association formed by countries or groups who want to support one another

capture – to take someone prisoner

civilisation – a society or culture that is highly developed

enemy – someone who seeks to harm another

molasses – a dark brown syrup made from sugar cane

plantation – a large area of land where certain crops are grown, e.g., sugar, tea

punish – to make someone suffer because they have done wrong

slave – a person who is owned by another person and works without being paid

surrender – to give yourself up to an enemy

traitor – someone who betrays his or her country or friends, by helping the enemy

truce – an agreement to stop fighting for a while

withdraw – to pull back from a place or people